DISNEY LEARNING

Disney

MOANA

AGES

5-6

KEY STAGE 1

English
Practice

S0-AUZ-456

© 2017 Disney Enterprises, Inc. All rights reserved.

Scholastic Children's Books
Euston House,
24 Eversholt Street,
London NW1 1DB, UK

A division of Scholastic Ltd
London • New York • Toronto • Sydney • Auckland
Mexico City • New Delhi • Hong Kong

Book packaging by Blooberry Design

Published in the UK by Scholastic Ltd, 2017

ISBN 978 1 4071 6492 2

Printed in the UK by Bell and Bain Ltd, Glasgow

2 4 6 8 10 9 7 5 3 1

All rights reserved

This book is sold subject to the condition that it shall not, by way of trade or otherwise be lent, resold, hired out, or otherwise circulated without the publisher's prior consent in any form or binding other than that in which it is published and without a similar condition, including this condition, being imposed upon the subsequent purchaser.

Papers used by Scholastic Children's Books are made from wood grown in sustainable forests.

www.scholastic.co.uk

Welcome to the Disney Learning Programme!

Children learn best when they are having fun!

The **Disney Learning Workbooks** are an engaging way for your child to develop their English skills with fun characters from the wonderful world of Disney.

The **Disney Learning Workbooks** are carefully levelled to present new challenges to developing learners. This workbook has been designed to support the National Curriculum for English at Key Stage 1, and offers children the opportunity to practise skills learned at school and to consolidate their learning in a relaxed home setting with parental support. Stickers, motivating story pages and a range of activities related to the film *Moana*, will ensure that your child has fun while improving their handwriting, reading and spelling.

As children learn to write, they must bring together many skills. They need to develop handwriting with correct letter formation, learn how to structure sentences and use basic punctuation, and spell words with many different spelling patterns. Each of these skills takes time to master and practice is crucial. These skills will become the foundation of children's writing and will ensure that they can communicate all their wonderful ideas and stories.

This book includes 'Let's Read' stories featuring characters from the film *Moana* for you and your child to share. Keep practice sessions fun and short. Reading instructions together will ensure your child knows what to do before starting.

Have fun with the Disney Learning Programme!

Developed in conjunction with Charlotte Raby, educational consultant

Let's Practise Reading and Writing

In this book, you will find lots of activities to help you practise reading and writing. You will meet these tricky words:

he	do	to	today	of	this
says	were	was	is	his	has
are	you	they	go	be	yes
she	I	no	so	by	me
here	there	where	love	some	one
can	ask	friend	school	put	up
full	climb	our	your	push	a

Tips to Help

- Work on a flat surface. If you are left-handed, turn your paper like this:

- Find somewhere quiet to work.

- Make sure you have lots of space when you write.

- Don't worry about making a mistake – it's part of how we all learn! Just cross it out and try again.

- You can check your answers on pages 44 to 46.

Let's Talk About the Characters

You'll meet all these characters in Moana's story.
Can you say their names out loud? The letters in blue
tell you how to say the names correctly.

Maui
(**mau**-ee)

Tui
(**too**-ee)

Tala
(**tah**-la)

Moana
(**moh**-ah-na)

Pua
(**pooh**-ah)

Heihei
(**hay**-hay)

Tamatoa
(**tam**-ah-toh-ah)

Now write each character's name, then find the matching stickers.

Maui

Tui

Tala

Moana

Pua

Heihei

Tamatoa

Motunui
moh-too-noo-ee

In the middle of the ocean lay the beautiful island of Motunui. For centuries, the island gave the villagers everything they needed to lead happy lives.

Legend told of an island goddess called Te Fiti. Her heart had the power to create life itself, and Te Fiti shared her gift with the world. But there were some who wanted to take Te Fiti's heart, and use its powerful magic for themselves.

Maui was a demigod. His magical fish hook let him change shape. One day, Maui used his fish hook to transform into a huge hawk and he stole Te Fiti's heart! But, as Maui tried to fly away, he was struck from the sky by an enormous demon of fire and earth called Te Kā. Maui, his hook and the heart vanished into the sea.

One thousand years later, storytellers still share the tale of Maui and Te Fiti's heart – of how darkness spread across the islands causing animals and plants to die and chasing away all the fish.

"One day, the heart will be found," Gramma Tala told the island's children, "by someone who will journey beyond our reef, find Maui and bring him back across the ocean to restore Te Fiti's heart."

All the children were scared – except one. Gramma Tala's young granddaughter, Moana, smiled and clapped with delight at the story.

Read the questions together with a grown-up and talk about the story.

1   Who stole Te Fiti's heart? Why?

2   If you had Maui's magical hook what would you transform into? Why?

3   What do you think will happen next?

Can you draw a picture of your answer to question 3?

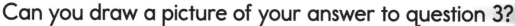

Moana needs your help!
Read the colour words, then choose colours
to brighten up her world.

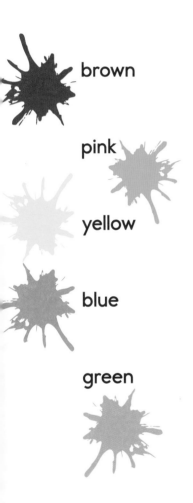

brown

pink

yellow

blue

green

Lower-case Letter Family 1

The letters l, t, i, j, u and y start at the top and go straight down.
Trace each letter. Start at the red dots and follow the arrows.

Tamatoa

Lower-case Letter Family 2

These letters all have a round shape in them.
Start at the red dots and follow the arrows.

Gramma Tala

Lower-case Letter Family 3

These letters all start at the top, go down and then back up again.
Start at the red dots and follow the arrows.

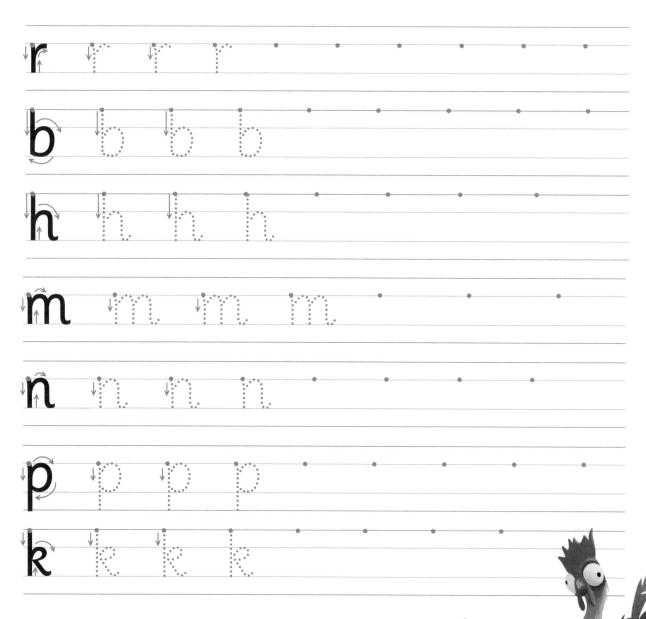

Heihei

The Rest of the Letters

These letters aren't in a letter family, because they are all formed slightly differently. Start at the red dots and follow the arrows.

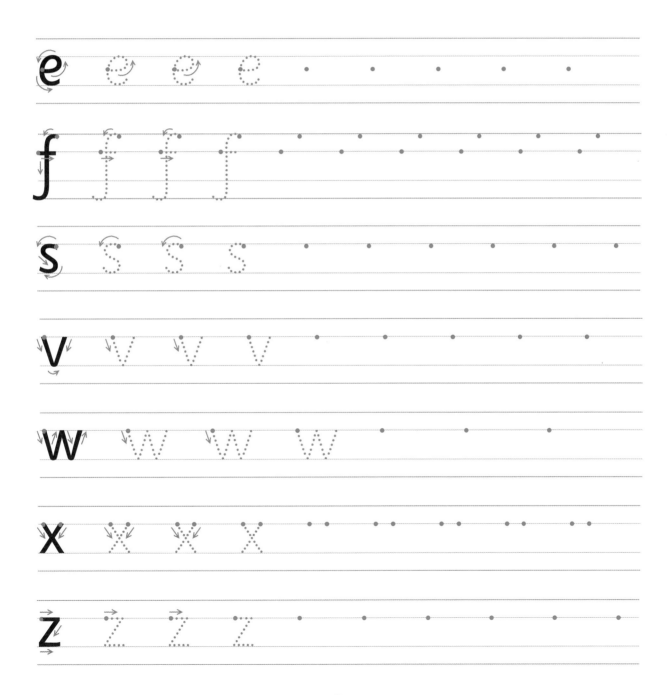

Let's Listen to Vowel Sounds

Say the words out loud and listen for the vowel sounds. Circle the words that have short vowel sounds.

beard

teeth

rock

Pages 42-43

Page 24

DISNEP
MOANA
© Disney

cloud

There are five short vowel sounds. They can be found in the words van, egg, hill, song and fun.

There are lots of long vowel sounds. They can be found in words such as: three, play, high and boat.

tree

pink

sand

sea

shell

17

Let's Use Tricky Words in a Sentence

Write the missing word to complete each sentence.

| friend | like | tonight | she |

a Moana's best

.... is called Pua.

b Gramma Tala is happy when

.... is telling stories.

c Moana is sailing her

boat ....

d Pua and Heihei ....

to play together.

Read the sentence and look at the picture. Decide if the sentence describes what is happening, then tick yes or no.

a Maui says he is strong.

yes   no

b Moana has two paddles.

yes   no

c Heihei has four legs.

yes   no

d Pua is a pig.

yes   no

Let's Learn Capital Letters in Order

When we say the alphabet, we use the letter names. Say them out loud.

Trace over each capital letter, starting at the red dot. Then write it yourself.

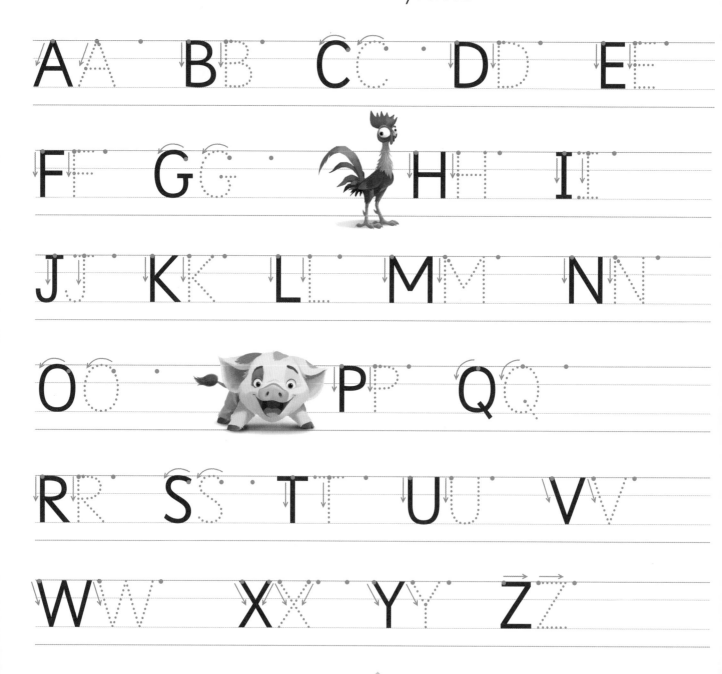

A A   B B   C C   D D   E E

F F   G G   H H   I I

J J   K K   L L   M M   N N

O O   P P   Q Q

R R   S S   T T   U U   V V

W W   X X   Y Y   Z Z

All sentences must start with a capital letter.
Full stops let us know that it is the end of a sentence.

Can you rewrite these sentences so that each one starts
with a capital letter and ends with a full stop?

the fish hook is magic

_____

_____

_____

moana has a leaf

_____

_____

_____

pua loves to eat

_____

_____

_____

tui is Moana's dad

_____

_____

_____

The years passed, and Moana grew into a young lady. Chief Tui, Moana's father, wanted Moana to stay and lead the villagers, but the ocean was calling. It was time for Moana to leave Motunui and find Maui. She would set sail, as her ancestors had done before her.

Moana went to the cavern of the wayfinders, and pushed one of the boats out into the water. A glowing manta ray swam quickly under Moana's boat, then leapt over the reef. It was a sign – Moana must follow! Taking a deep breath, she steered her boat behind the fish, over the reef and out into the open sea.

Brave Moana sailed all night, with only the stars to show her the way. She soon found that it wasn't easy to steer a boat in the open water, and it was harder still to follow a constellation that looked like a fish hook.

When the sun rose the next morning, Moana discovered that she had a stowaway! Heihei, the silly rooster, had hidden himself on board!

As the tide grew stronger, Moana became tired. She called to the ocean, but the ocean wouldn't help. Suddenly, a storm broke. The sky went dark, and huge waves crashed over the boat, sweeping Moana and Heihei into the water. Eventually, tired but safe, they landed on a small, rocky island.

The island was so quiet that Moana thought that it was deserted. Then she noticed a giant hook, carved in a boulder... Moana had washed up on Maui's island!

Let's Tell a Story

Think about the story you have just read.

Who were the characters? Find the matching stickers and write their names.

a _____

b _____

c _____

Draw a picture of Moana's boat here.

Read the sentences below. Put them in the right order, starting with number 1.

a Moana and Heihei get caught in a storm.

b Little Moana always delighted in Gramma Tala's stories of the island.

c But Moana sets sail on a journey to save her village instead.

d Chief Tui wants Moana to be the leader of the village.

e When Moana saw the giant hook carved in a boulder, she knew she was on Maui's island.

Let's Learn Words with the Long a Sound

Let's try a new sound! These words all have the long a sound. Look at the different spellings of the long a sound below. Can you sort the words into the right boxes?

If the spelling is a_e, you will also need a consonant. For example, take.

snake sail bake play grey
say rain ape again they

ay

ey

a_e

ai

We always start a sentence with a capital letter,
but some other words have capital letters too.

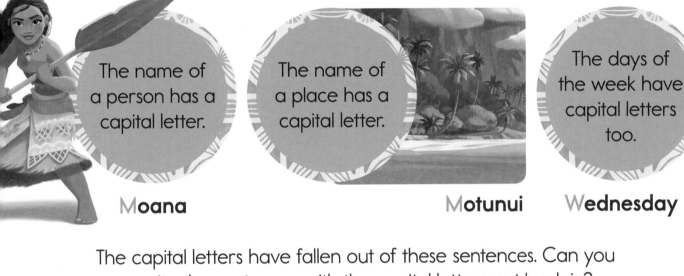

The name of a person has a capital letter.

Moana

The name of a place has a capital letter.

Motunui

The days of the week have capital letters too.

Wednesday

The capital letters have fallen out of these sentences. Can you rewrite the sentences with the capital letters put back in?

a moana sails on saturdays.

b pua and heihei can climb up.

c tamatoa lives in lalotai.

Let's Spell Words for Feelings

Trace over the letters to spell the feelings words.
Then find the right sticker to match each feeling.

a angry

b surprised

c scared

d tired

e love

f happy

Let's try a new sound! These words all have the long o sound. Look at the different spellings of the long o sound. Can you sort the words into the right boxes?

If the spelling is o_e, you will also need a consonant. For example, rope.

boat   slow   stone
toe   toast   blow   yellow
road   code   doe

oe

o_e

oa

ow

Let's Learn Words with the Long i Sound

Let's try a new sound! These words all have the long i sound. Look at the different spellings of the long i sound. Can you sort the words into the right boxes?

> bright   high   kite
> pie   try   light   why
> tie   fly   bike

If the spelling is i_e, you will also need a consonant. For example, bite.

i_e

ie

igh

y

Each of the words below names something in the picture. Can you write the correct one in each of the boxes?

sail   boat   wave   rope   sea

As Maui towered over her, Moana got to her feet. In her bravest voice, she began the speech that she had practised over and over. "Maui, shape-shifter, demigod of the wind and sea," she said loudly, "I am Moana of Motunui and—"

But Maui wasn't listening. He seized Moana's boat and held it high above his head. Then he told Moana tale after tale of all the great things he had done, without pausing for breath! Stories about how he had brought fire to humans and made the days longer by lassoing the sun. Maui even claimed that he had created coconuts!

Next, Maui showed off his tattoos. A mini Maui tattoo came to life, and danced magically among the other markings. Moana felt cross. Every time she tried to speak, Maui thought Moana was about to thank him for all his heroic deeds. After all, he was the mighty Maui – demigod and hero to all humans!

Then, after a while, Moana couldn't help but be charmed by Maui. She even began to enjoy his stories. Maui promised to show Moana something special inside a cave, but it was a trick! When Moana's back was turned, Maui fled from the cave, and rolled a giant boulder in front of the entrance. Moana was trapped!

Maui went back to the shore to find Moana's boat. At last, he could get off the island, and go in search of his magical fish hook.

Let's Write Questions

A sentence that asks a question ends with a question mark. Draw a line to join each question to its answer.

 **a** Who is Moana's father?

 **1** She followed a glowing manta ray.

b What sign did Moana follow?

2 He wanted to steal Te Fiti's heart.

c What kind of animal is Heihei?

3 Chief Tui is Moana's father.

d Why did Maui turn into a hawk?

4 Heihei is a rooster.

Look at this picture. Write a question to match this answer. Don't forget the question mark!

Answer:
Moana is clapping her hands.

34

Let's try a new sound! These words all have the long e sound. Look at the different spellings of the long e sound. Can you sort the words into the right boxes?

> eat money piece
> beach tree sea feet
> monkey green field

ey

ie

ea

ee

Let's Learn Tricky Words

Read these tricky words out loud.

he	me	she	no	be
was	push	our	you	ask

For every word you read, colour in a bug.
Start at number 1 and keep going until
you reach number 10.

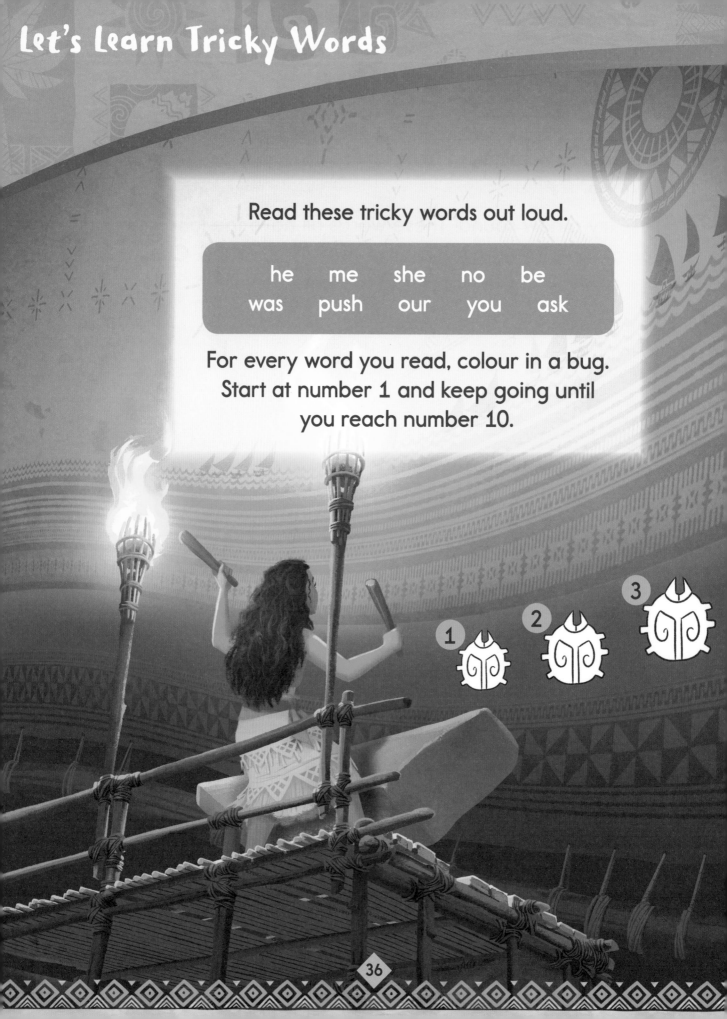

Let's Make a Kakamori Mask

In the film, Maui and Moana meet the Kakamori. The Kakamori wear masks.

Try making your own fearsome Kakamori mask!

What to do:

1. Colour in the front of your mask.
2. Carefully tear out the page and glue it on to the piece of card.
3. Ask a grown-up to help you cut the mask out.
4. Then ask your grown-up to help you cut out the eyes and pierce a hole in each side of the mask.
5. Thread the string or elastic through the holes.
6. Hold the mask over your face and ask your grown-up to tie it on!

You will need:

- a piece of thin card
- scissors
- glue
- colouring pens, pencils or crayons
- string or elastic long enough to go around your head

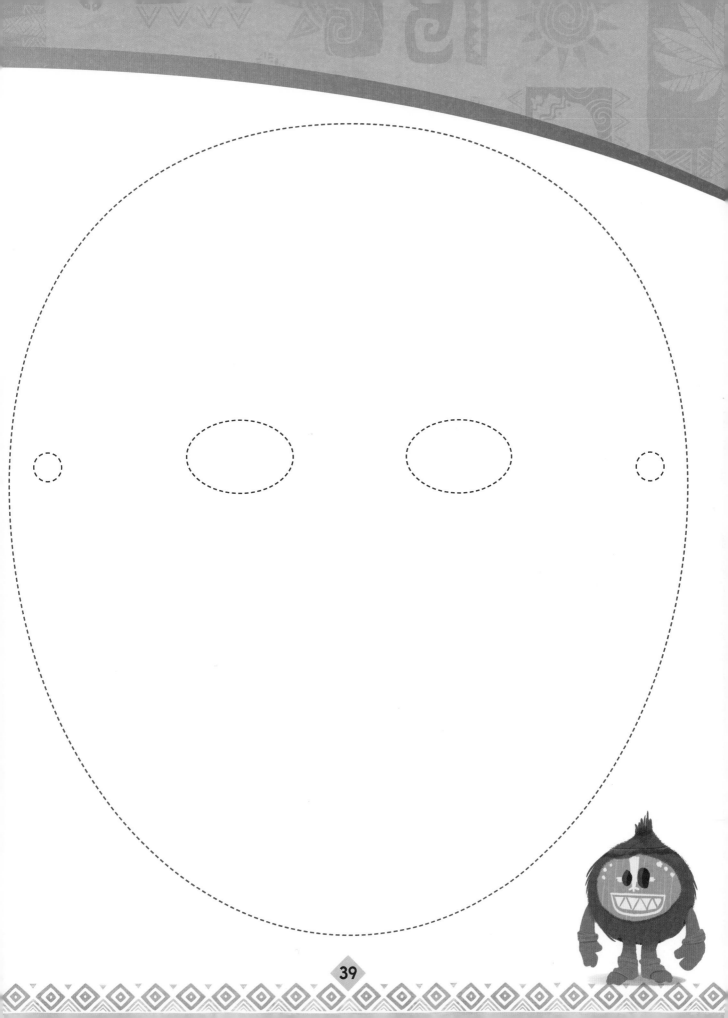

Choose the right tools

Having the right tools can make a big difference to children. Try out different pens and pencils – fibre-tip pens that glide over the page can really help young writers gain pen control. The right type of paper can make a big difference, too. Try to find paper that is smooth and easy to write on and make sure the paper isn't too shiny, or it can be hard for your child to control their pen. Consider ergonomic pens and pencils, especially if your child is left-handed.

Encourage your child to form the letters correctly – starting in the right place and flowing to the end of the letter. Correct letter formation will really help children write with greater fluency. This will help them later, when they begin to do joined-up handwriting.

Find opportunities to write

When children are learning to write, they must bring together many different skills – spelling, handwriting, sequencing and thinking! Children will develop these skills over time, and sometimes one facet of their development will be faster than the others. This is normal.

Make writing fun. Get large pieces of paper and encourage your child to write and draw, filling up the space. This will help children gain control of their fine motor skills. Draw spirals and circles and ask your child to trace over them. Then encourage your child's efforts.

Write and draw with your child. You could both draw their favourite toy or story character, and label them.

Ask your child to help you write lists, invitations and cards, to show that writing is an everyday and purposeful activity.

Retell stories together. Map out the story or make comic strips, writing simple sentences to tell the story.

Here Are All the Things I Can Do

Place a star sticker next to the things that you can do!

I can write ...

letters from lower-case family 1

letters from lower-case family 2

letters from lower-case family 3

zig-zag and curvy letters

capital letters

I can ...

check that sentences make sense

I can read and spell tricky words ...

Tick the box next to the words you can read and spell

he		do		to		today		of		this	
says		were		was		is		his		has	
are		you		they		go		be		yes	
she		I		no		so		by		me	
here		there		where		love		some		one	
can		ask		friend		school		put		up	
full		climb		our		your		push		a	

I can spell words with ...

the long a sound,
(ay, ai, a_e and ey)

the long e sound,
(ee, ea, ie, ey)

the long o sound,
(ow, oa, o_e, oe)

the long i sound,
(igh, ie, i_e, y)

I can write ...

sentences with capital
letters and a full stop

questions

labels

I can ...

retell a story

remember characters'
names

talk about how
characters feel

Answers

Page 10

Help children to find the parts of the story that will help them answer. Then ask them for the reasons for their answers.

Pages 16–17

The short vowel sounds are: sand, rock, pink and shell.

Page 18

a. Moana's best friend is called Pua.
b. Gramma Tala is happy when she is telling stories.
c. Moana is sailing her boat tonight.
d. Pua and Heihei like to play together.

Page 19

a. Maui says he is strong.   yes
b. Moana has two paddles.   no
c. Heihei has four legs.   no
d. Pua is a pig.   yes

Page 21

a. The fish hook is magic.
b. Moana has a leaf.
c. Pua loves to eat.
d. Tui is Moana's dad.

Page 24

a. Tui
b. Moana
c. Heihei

Page 25

1   b. Little Moana always delighted in Gramma Tala's stories of the island.
2   d. Chief Tui wants Moana to be the leader of the village.
3   c. But Moana sets sail on a journey to save her village instead.
4   a. Moana and Heihei get caught in a storm.
5   e. When Moana saw the giant hook carved in a boulder she knew she was on Maui's island.

Page 26

ay		ey
play		grey
say		they

a_e		ai
snake		sail
bake		rain
ape		again

Page 27

a. Moana sails on Saturdays.

b. Pua and Heihei can climb up.

c. Tamatoa lives in Lalotai.

Page 28

angry

surprised

scared

tired

love

happy

Page 29

oe
toe
doe

o_e
stone
code

oa
boat
toast
road

ow
slow
blow
yellow

Page 30

i_e
kite
bike

ie
pie
tie

igh
bright
high
light

y
try
why
fly

Answers

Page 31

sail · rope · boat · wave · sea

Page 34

a. 3 c. 4
b. 1 d. 2

e. What is Moana doing?
   (*Suggested answer*)

Page 35

ey
money
monkey

ie
piece
field

ea
eat
beach
sea

ee
tree
feet
green

Disney
MOANA

CONGRATULATIONS

....

(Name)

has completed the Disney Learning Workbook:

English Practice

Presented on

....

(Date)

....

(Parent's Signature)

© 2017 Disney

© 2017 Disney